85

Songs for Little Singers No. 3

A Collection of Songs, Exercises and Recitations for use by the Childrens' Division and in the Home Circle.

Edited by Elsie Duncan Yale

The RODEHEAVER Co.
HALL-MACK
WINONA LAKE, INDIANA

PRINTED IN U.S.A.

PREFACE

The cordial and appreciative welcome given to *Songs for Little Singers Nos. 1 and 2* has been a pleasant incentive to the preparation of a third volume of songs for children.

As in the preceding books, the songs are expressed in language well within the comprehension of any child, while the music is tuneful and of real merit.

The teacher will find especial help in the Musical Object Lessons (see Nos. 6-7-12), which we believe to be an entirely new idea in primary music. The truth taught by the song is emphasized by an illustrative exercise in which the children can participate.

One department of the book is entirely given over to special exercises which will aid the teacher in that most vital part of the work—the memorizing of the Scriptures.

So with sincere appreciation of the cordial welcome and commendation accorded to the previous books of the series, and with the earnest hope that No. 3 may indeed prove a help and inspiration, it is dedicated to the many little singers everywhere by

THE EDITOR.

Songs for Little Singers, No. 3.

We Come to Thee.

E. E. Hewitt.   Lida Shivers Leech.

1. Once to Je - sus came the moth - ers, Bring - ing Him their
2. In His ten - der arms He held them, Soft - ly touch - ing
3. Now we come to Thee, dear Sav - iour, Ask - ing Thee to

chil - dren dear; O the hap - py sto - ry, For the Lord of glo - ry,
ev - 'ry head; Giv - ing them His bless - ing, To His bo - som pressing,
bless us all; O the hap - py sto - ry. For the Lord of glo - ry,

REFRAIN.

Kind - ly smiled as they drew near. } We come, we
Ev - 'ry child the moth - ers led. } We come, we
Gives to us His gen - tle call. }

come; Sav - iour, we have come to Thee.

(3)

Someone Spoke a Pleasant Word.

ALICE JEAN CLEATOR.
 ARTHUR WILTON.

1. Some-one spoke a pleas-ant word, [1]Gave it where 'twas need-ed.
2. Words un-kind seem lit-tle things, [3]But, O fear to say them;

O how glad-ly some-one heard, And its mes-sage heed-ed.
Once they fly on out-ward [4]wings, [5]There's no pow'r can stay them.

CHORUS.

O how much 'twill mat-ter What our words shall scat-ter. [2]

May they scat-ter sun-shine Ev-'ry day.

MOTIONS.—1, Hold out hands as if giving. 2, Motion as if scattering seed. 3, Hand to heart. 4, Fluttering motion, both hands to represent flying. 5, Hands out as if entreating.

God Cares for Me.

ALICE JEAN CLEATOR.　　　　　FLORENCE WILLIAMS FALCONER.

1. Why are tree-tops sway-ing, [1] Wav-ing wel-come hands? Why are breezes stray-ing O'er the mead-ow lands? [2] Why are song-birds sing-ing Trill-ing in their glee? [3] O this word they're bringing, "He cares for me." [4]

2. Why are riv-ers shin-ing, [6] Winding many a mile? Why the clouds' gold lin-ing, [7] And the sun's bright smile? All the world is tell-ing Un-to you and me, "God on high is dwell-ing, He cares for me."

REFRAIN.

God on high is dwell-ing, [5] Send-ing gifts so free, And all things are tell-ing, "He cares for me."

MOTIONS.—1, Wave right hand. 2, Outward motion. 3, Point upward to right. 4, Point up 5, Hold out both hands, looking up. 6, Describe circular motions with right forefinger· 7, Same as No. 4.

Garden Messages.

Elsie Duncan Yale   Howard E. Smith.

1. In our gar-den we can find, Tokens of a King so kind,
2. Ros-es with their perfume sweet, Message of a King re-peat,
3. Grasses in their green so fair, Whisper of a Fa-ther's care,

Lil-ies in the leaf-y ways, Tell of Him we praise.
Blooming 'neath the sun-lit rays, Tell of Him we praise.
Stir-ring as the soft breeze strays, Tell of Him we praise.

CHORUS.

{ God is love, God is love, He is near though
{ O'er us all, O'er us all Is His care what-

throh'd above, Ev-er praise ye Him.
e'er be-fall Ev-er (Omit...........................) } praise ye Him !

NOTE.—During the singing of the first verse, a Child may hold a lily, and at its conclusion, place the flower in a vase. The verse, Matt. 6:28, is then repeated. During the second verse, a rose is held, and when it is placed in a vase, Song of Solomon 2:1 is repeated. During the third verse, grasses are held, and when they are placed in a vase, Matt. 6:30 is recited.

Little Lights

Elsie Duncan Yale.

Arthur Wilton.

1. I may be a light for Him, Shin-ing day by day,
2. If my light is bright and clear, Some one else may see,
3. Striv-ing just for Him to shine, Faith-ful I'll be found,

Gleam-ing bright and nev-er dim, Guid-ing in His way.
Learn to love my Sav-iour dear, Strive a light to be.
Try to send His light di-vine, Un-to those a-round.

REFRAIN.

Shin-ing, shin-ing, lit-tle lights are we,

Shin-ing, shin-ing, lov-ing Lord, for Thee.

NOTE.—If desired to use this song as an object lesson, the teacher may have several small candles or tapers. Before the first verse is sung, the first candle may be lighted. At the end of the first verse, light the second candle from the first, and at the end of the third verse, light several candles from the first two. The candle-lighting should not, of course, be done by the children.

Joyfully Singing.

E. E. HEWITT. (Posthumous.) WALTER A. SHAWKER.

1. The children were joy-ful-ly sing - ing, One beau-ti-ful day in
2. They gathered so glad-ly a-round Him, And scattered their brightest
3. His love is so constant and ten - der, We lift our hos-an-na-

spring; To Je-sus their voic-es were ring - ing, To
flow'rs; With gifts of our love we sur-round Him, And
psalms; A kind, lov-ing deed we can ren - der, Is

Je-sus, our Sav-iour, King.
give Him these hearts of ours.
bet-ter than wav-ing palms.

CHORUS.

A - gain all the children are sing -

ing; He list-ens and hears, we know; ... He smiles on the

praise we are bring - ing, As once in the long a - go. . . . .

Growing Like Jesus.

E. E. HEWITT. (Posthumous.) ARTHUR WILTON.

1. Je - sus was once a child like me, Pleas - ing His
2. Help us, dear Lord, to look a - bove, Shed - ding a -
3. He was a child like you and me; In Him our

par - ents faith - ful - ly; Show - ing a bright and smil - ing face,
round the light of love, Love that will bright - en ev - 'ry day,
love - ly Pat - tern see; Old - er and tall - er as we grow,

Mak - ing His home a hap - py place. ⎫
Love that will cheer an - oth - er's way. ⎬ More like Thee, more like Thee,
We would our love for Je - sus show. ⎭

CHORUS.

Dai - ly, like Je - sus, our Sav - iour to be, Love and o - bey,

fol - low Thy way, Grow - ing in wis - dom and more like Thee.

Praise the Lord.

E. E. HEWITT. (Posthumous.) FLORENCE WILLIAMS FALCONER.

1. Ros - es bright and snowflakes white, Tell a hap - py sto - ry;
2. Do the right, by day or night; Je - sus will de - fend us;
3. Trust the love that rules a - bove; God will safe - ly guide us;

To and fro the breez - es blow, To our Fa - ther's glo - ry.
Nev - er fear, for He is near, Read - y to be - friend us.
Sun - ny ways, or cloud - y days, Light will He pro - vide us.

CHORUS.

Praise the Lord, praise the Lord! Ma - ny voic - es tell....

God is near our prayer to hear, All He does is well.

Walk in Love.

E. E. Hewitt. (Posthumous.)   Arthur Wilton

1. O the hap - py birds and flow'rs would say, Be good,　be kind;
2. Hear a mes - sage from the stars of light, Be good,　be kind;
3. And the Fa - ther tells us in His word, Be good,　be kind;

Help-ing one an - oth - er ev - 'ry day, Be good,　be kind.
Tell - ing as they twin-kle, gold - en bright, Be good,　be kind.
In our hearts a whis-per we have heard, Be good,　be kind.

Chorus.

Walk in love, walk in love, In the love of Christ, our Sav-iour,

Walk in love, walk in love, Prais - ing God a - bove.

Wondrous Stories.

Elsie Duncan Yale.   (Parable Song)   A. A. Payn.

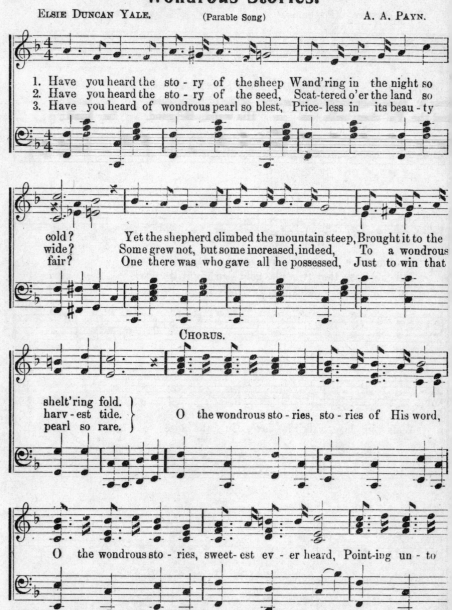

1. Have you heard the sto-ry of the sheep Wand'ring in the night so
2. Have you heard the sto-ry of the seed, Scat-tered o'er the land so
3. Have you heard of wondrous pearl so blest, Price-less in its beau-ty

cold? Yet the shepherd climbed the mountain steep, Brought it to the
wide? Some grew not, but some increased, indeed, To a wondrous
fair? One there was who gave all he possessed, Just to win that

Chorus.

shelt'ring fold.)
harv-est tide. > O the wondrous sto-ries, sto-ries of His word,
pearl so rare.)

O the wondrous sto-ries, sweet-est ev-er heard, Point-ing un-to

Note.—This song may be illustrated by objects. While the first verse is sung a teacher or a child
may hold up the picture of a sheep. As the second verse is sung, seeds may be displayed, and during
the singing of the third verse, a large pearl bead may be shown. The song may be preceded by the
telling of the parables mentioned. Luke 15: 3-10. Mark 4: 3-20. Matthew 13: 45, 46.

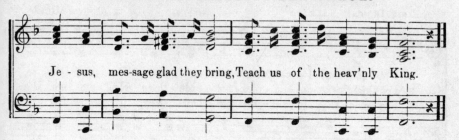

Je - sus, mes-sage glad they bring, Teach us of the heav'nly King.

Break Thou the Bread of Life.

M. A. LATHBURY.   W. F. SHERWIN.

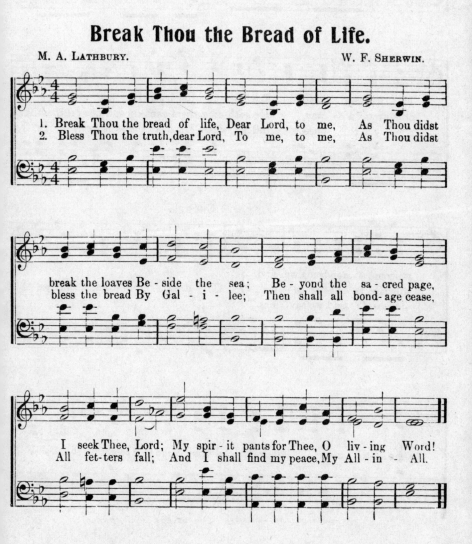

1. Break Thou the bread of life, Dear Lord, to me, As Thou didst
2. Bless Thou the truth, dear Lord, To me, to me, As Thou didst

break the loaves Be - side the sea; Be - yond the sa - cred page,
bless the bread By Gal - i - lee; Then shall all bond - age cease,

I seek Thee, Lord; My spir - it pants for Thee, O liv - ing Word!
All fet - ters fall; And I shall find my peace, My All - in - All.

Children, Come.

Elsie Duncan Yale.   C. Austin Miles.

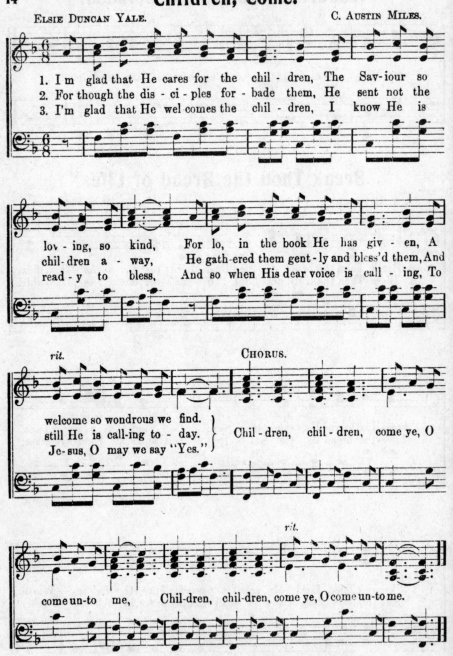

1. I'm glad that He cares for the chil-dren, The Sav-iour so
2. For though the dis-ci-ples for-bade them, He sent not the
3. I'm glad that He wel-comes the chil-dren, I know He is

lov - ing, so   kind,   For lo, in the book He has giv - en, A
chil-dren a - way,   He gath-ered them gent-ly and bless'd them, And
read - y to   bless,   And so when His dear voice is call - ing, To

welcome so wondrous we find.
still He is call-ing to - day.   } Chil-dren,   chil-dren,   come ye, O
Je-sus, O may we say "Yes."

come un-to me,   Chil-dren, chil-dren, come ye, O come un-to me.

He is Calling.

G. W. Payn. ARTHUR WILTON.

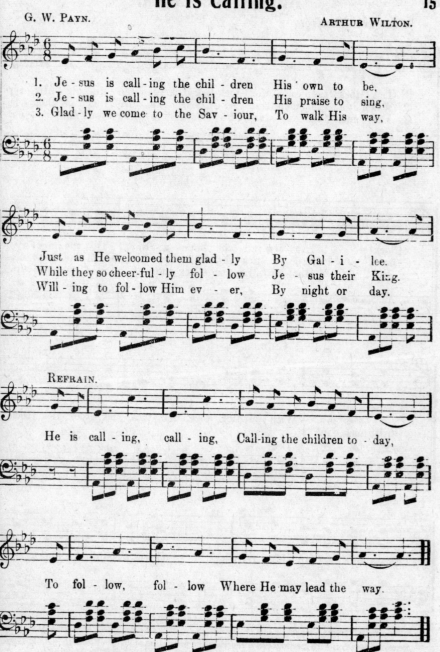

1. Je - sus is call - ing the chil - dren His own to be,
2. Je - sus is call - ing the chil - dren His praise to sing,
3. Glad - ly we come to the Sav - iour, To walk His way,

Just as He welcomed them glad - ly By Gal - i - lee.
While they so cheer-ful - ly fol - low Je - sus their King.
Will - ing to fol - low Him ev - er, By night or day.

REFRAIN.

He is call - ing, call - ing, Call-ing the children to - day,

To fol - low, fol - low Where He may lead the way.

Hurry, Mr. Clock.

ALICE JEAN CLEATOR.

C. AUSTIN MILES.

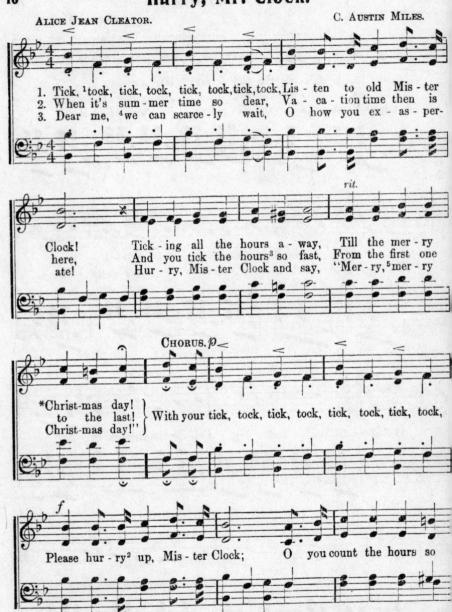

1. Tick, tock, tick, tock, tick, tock, tick, tock, Lis - ten to old Mis - ter
2. When it's sum - mer time so dear, Va - ca - tion time then is
3. Dear me, we can scarce - ly wait, O how you ex - as - per-

Clock! Tick - ing all the hours a - way, Till the mer - ry
here, And you tick the hours so fast, From the first one
ate! Hur - ry, Mis - ter Clock and say, "Mer - ry, mer - ry

CHORUS.

*Christ-mas day!   }
to the last!   } With your tick, tock, tick, tock, tick, tock, tick, tock,
Christ-mas day!"   }

Please hur - ry up, Mis - ter Clock;   O you count the hours so

* The words "happy Children's Day," "Easter Day," or "Holiday," may be substituted.

MOTIONS.—Motion with forefinger as if representing pendulum of clock. 2, Stamp foot. 3, Motion as if counting on fingers. 4, Hands clasped in impatience. 5, Hands extended, smiling.

Hurry, Mr. Clock.—Concluded.

p

slow! Can't you make them fast-er, fast-er go? With your tick, tock,

f

tick, tock, tick, tock, tick, tock, Please hur-ry up, Mis-ter Clock.

Little Workers.

G. W. PAYN.   ARTHUR WILTON

1. We are lit-tle work-ers For our lov-ing King, All we
2. Bus-y lit-tle fin-gers, Ten in all have we, In the
3. Eyes to look to Je-sus, Ears to hear His call, Lips to

REFRAIN.

have we of-fer, All to Him we bring.
Mas-ter's serv-ice, Bus-y as can be.   Je-sus, Je-sus,
sing His prais-es, He will bless them all.

Keep us ev-'ry day, Work-ing, liv-ing, In Thy bless-ed way.

Though We Are But Children.

ALICE JEAN CLEATOR.   FLORENCE WILLIAMS FALCONER.

1. Tho' we are but chil-dren, Something we can do, If our hands are
will-ing, And our hearts are true.

2. We are on-ly chil-dren, We're not ver-y tall, We can serve the
Sav-iour, Tho' we may be small.

3. Je-sus called the chil-dren In the long a-go, And we know He'll
help us, As we on-ward go.

REFRAIN.

Tho' we are but chil-dren, there is some-thing we can do, If our hearts are right, If our hearts are true. We can all be read-y, each our Fa-ther's will to do, And some day we'll be grown-ups, too.

Scattering Seeds of Kindness.

W. A. S.

WALTER A. SHAWKER.

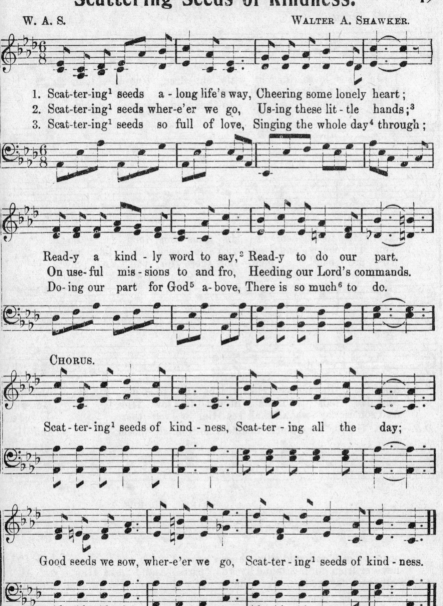

1. Scat-ter-ing[1] seeds a-long life's way, Cheering some lonely heart;
2. Scat-ter-ing[1] seeds wher-e'er we go, Us-ing these lit-tle hands;[3]
3. Scat-ter-ing[1] seeds so full of love, Singing the whole day[4] through;

Read-y a kind-ly word to say,[2] Read-y to do our part.
On use-ful mis-sions to and fro, Heeding our Lord's commands.
Do-ing our part for God[5] a-bove, There is so much[6] to do.

CHORUS.

Scat-ter-ing[1] seeds of kind-ness, Scat-ter-ing all the day;

Good seeds we sow, wher-e'er we go, Scat-ter-ing[1] seeds of kind-ness.

MOTIONS.—1, Scattering motion of seeds. 2, Touch lips with right hand. 3, Hold hands out, palms up. 4, Open arms wide. 5, Point up, look up. 6, Lay right hand on heart.

Copyright, MCMXIX, by Hall-Mack Co. International Copyright Secured.

I Love Him.

Lida S. Leech.

A. A. Payn.

1. Je - sus loves the lit - tle chil - dren, I've been told,
2. Je - sus makes the chil - dren hap - py, as of yore,
3. He has gone a - way to heav - en, I've been told,

For He took them in His arms long, long a - go;
For He comes and dwells with - in each lit - tle heart;
To pre - pare a man - sion there for you and me;

And the Bi - ble says He's with us still, to - day, And His
And He tells us if we'll al - ways fol - low Him, He will
And some day we all shall see Him o - ver there, If we
D.S.—He is al - ways near to shield us from all harm, And He

FINE. CHORUS.

lov - ing care and guid - ance we can know.
nev - er from our hearts and lives de - part. } And I love Him, yes, I
strive each day we live, like Him to be.
ev - er lis - tens to the faint - est call.

I Love Him.—Concluded.

D.S.

21

love Him, He is the chil-dren's Friend, and loves them all;

Flowers Bright.

G. W. PAYN.

ARTHUR WILTON.

1. In the field and for-est flow-ers fair, Grow-ing, grow-ing;
2. In the gar-den of the Lord are we, Grow-ing, grow-ing;

Send a fra-grance sweet up-on the air, Grow-ing, grow-ing.
Flow-ers for His serv-ice glad to be, Grow-ing, grow-ing,

CHORUS.

Flow-ers bright, grow-ing for the King, Sweet and fair, ev-'ry-where;

So are we growing for the King, In His gar-den fair.

Every One Here.

ALICE JEAN CLEATOR.　　　　　　　　　　WALTER A. SHAWKER.

1. Bells to-day are [1]ring - ing, Ring - ing, swing - ing;
2. Bells to-day are [5]sway - ing, Sway - ing, sway - ing;
3. Bells to-day are call - ing, [7]Ech - oes fall - ing;

Bells to-day are sing - ing, [2]Wel - come! Wel - come!
Bells to-day are say - ing, [6]Wel - come! Wel - come!
Bells to-day are call - ing, [8]Wel - come! Wel - come!

CHORUS.

[3]Wel-come to - day to the Sun - day School, "Ev - 'ry one

here," [4]let this be our rule— "Ev - 'ry one here,

MOTIONS.—1, Upward swinging motion with right arm. 2, Hands extended. 3, Same as two. 4, Outward motion with right hand. 5, Same as one. 6, Same as two. 7, Right hand held up slowly descending. 8, Same as two.

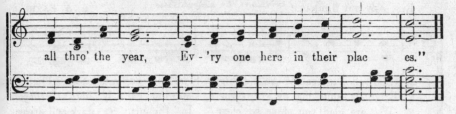

all thro' the year, Ev-'ry one here in their plac - es."

Little Sunbeams.

W. A. S.

WALTER A. SHAWKER.

1. We are lit - tle sun - beams, Beam - ing bright and gay;
2. We will shine for Je - sus, Ev - 'ry-where we go;

Joy - ful - ly we're sing - ing, On this hap - py day.
Scatt'ring bless - ed sun - shine, In this world be - low.

CHORUS.

We are lit - tle sun - beams, Bright and fair, ev - 'ry-where;

We are lit - tle sun - beams, In the Fa - ther's care.

Just Like You.

Rev. Alfred Barratt.

A. A. Payn.

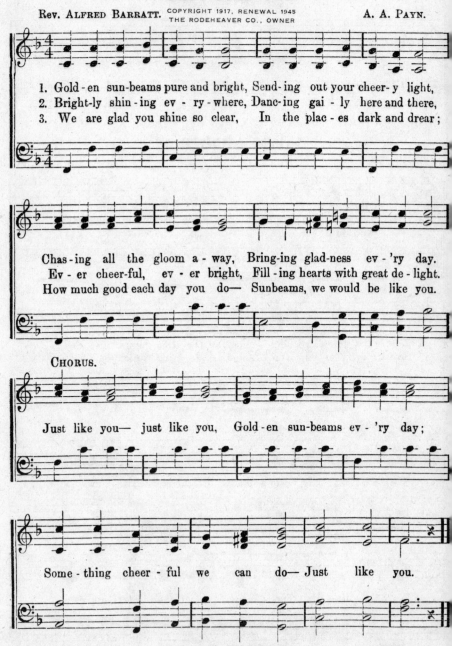

1. Gold-en sun-beams pure and bright, Send-ing out your cheer-y light,
2. Bright-ly shin-ing ev-ry-where, Danc-ing gai-ly here and there,
3. We are glad you shine so clear, In the plac-es dark and drear;

Chas-ing all the gloom a-way, Bring-ing glad-ness ev-'ry day.
Ev-er cheer-ful, ev-er bright, Fill-ing hearts with great de-light.
How much good each day you do— Sunbeams, we would be like you.

CHORUS.

Just like you— just like you, Gold-en sun-beams ev-'ry day;

Some-thing cheer-ful we can do— Just like you.

Serving My Saviour.

Lida S. Leech.

Arthur Wilton.

1. Two lit - tle ¹hands for the Mas - ter, Serv - ing so true;
2. Two lit - tle ²ears ev - er o - pen, Hear - ing each day;
3. Two lit - tle ³eyes see - ing Je - sus, In ev - 'ry - thing;
4. Two lit - tle ⁵feet ev - er walk - ing In paths of right;

By lit - tle acts of kind - ness Which I may do.
Something to make me stron - ger, In God's own way.
One hap - py ⁴heart that's prais - ing, Je - sus my King.
Foll'wing the lov - ing Sav - iour, Led in the light.

Refrain.

Serv - ing my Sav - iour, Faith - ful and true;

Speak words for Je - sus, Kind, lov - ing deeds I'll do.

Motions.—1, Hold hands out, palms up. 2, Tips of fingers to ears. 3, Tips of fingers to eyes.
4, Right hand on heart. 5, Right foot forward.

26 Dwell in My Heart.

Elsie Duncan Yale. G. W. Payn.

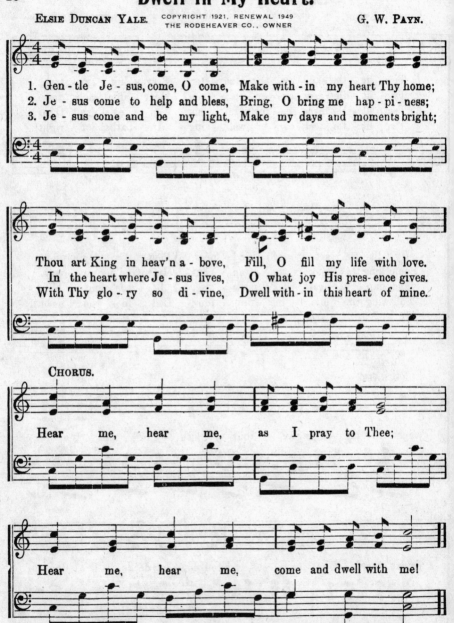

1. Gen - tle Je - sus, come, O come, Make with - in my heart Thy home;
2. Je - sus come to help and bless, Bring, O bring me hap - pi - ness;
3. Je - sus come and be my light, Make my days and moments bright;

Thou art King in heav'n a - bove, Fill, O fill my life with love.
In the heart where Je - sus lives, O what joy His pres - ence gives.
With Thy glo - ry so di - vine, Dwell with - in this heart of mine.

CHORUS.

Hear me, hear me, as I pray to Thee;

Hear me, hear me, come and dwell with me!

NOTE.—Before this song is sung, the teacher should draw the outline of a heart on the blackboard.
After the first verse write in it "LOVE," after the second, "JOY" after the third, "LIGHT."

To Learn of Thee

LIDA S. LEECH.

ARTHUR WILTON

1. The Sab-bath bells are ring - ing, And call-ing you and me;
2. We glad - ly sing Thy prais - es, We're hap - py as can be;
3. Be with us while we tar - ry, Thy lov-ing chil - dren, we;

To gath - er in Thy tem - ple, To learn, dear Lord of Thee.
That we are here to - geth - er, To learn, dear Lord of Thee.
For O what joy it gives us, To learn, dear Lord of Theo.

REFRAIN.

Just to learn of Thee, Just to learn of Thee;

We gath - er here dear Je - sus, To learn of Thee.

We Are Glad.

LIDA S. LEECH.　　　　　　　　　　　　　　WALTER A. SHAWKER.

1. The sun-beams are danc-ing for glad - ness, The bird - ies are
2. The flow - ers are bloom-ing in beau - ty, The riv - u - lets
3. We sing with the trees and the blos - soms, The sun and the

sing ing sweet songs; And we are so hap-py, for Je - sus With
sing by the way; And we are so hap py, for Je - sus Cares
birds as they wing; All na-ture is sing-ing His prais - es, The

glad - ness fills all the day long.
for His dear chil - dren al - way.
joy - bells of hap - pi - ness ring.

CHORUS.

We are glad, we are

glad, Sing - ing His prais - es the whole day long; We are

glad, we are glad, Fill - ing the world with our hap - py song.

Jesus Calls.

E. E. HEWITT. (Posthumous.)   ARTHUR WILTON.

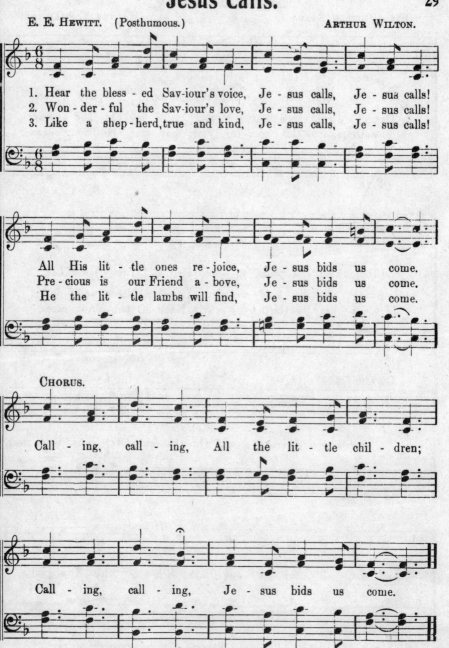

1. Hear the bless - ed Sav-iour's voice, Je - sus calls, Je - sus calls!
2. Won - der - ful the Sav-iour's love, Je - sus calls, Je - sus calls!
3. Like a shep - herd, true and kind, Je - sus calls, Je - sus calls!

All His lit - tle ones re - joice, Je - sus bids us come.
Pre - cious is our Friend a - bove, Je - sus bids us come.
He the lit - tle lambs will find, Je - sus bids us come.

CHORUS.

Call - ing, call - ing, All the lit - tle chil - dren;

Call - ing, call - ing, Je - sus bids us come.

Birthday Song.

ELSIE DUNCAN YALE.　　　　　　　　　　　WALTER A. SHAWKER.

1. Je - sus hear our birth-day pray'r, Keep (him/her) in Thy care,
2. Grant Thy guid-ance day by day, Lead-ing in Thy way,
3. Bless throughout this com-ing year, Sav-iour, be Thou near;

And through all the years to be, Help (him/her) fol-low Thee.

Help-ing to be kind and true, Lov-ing deeds to do.

Je - sus hear this birth-day pray'r, Keep in ten-d'rest care.

CHORUS.

Je - sus hear, Je - sus hear, On this birth-day be Thou near,

And may all the com-ing days, Ech - o with Thy praise.

NOTE.—To be sung after the child has placed his or her offering in the birthday box.

Long Ago.

ELSIE DUNCAN YALE. JOHN J. THOMAS.

1. Child - ren came their Sav - iour seek - ing, Long a - go, long a - go,
2. O the ten - der bless - ing giv - en, Long a - go, long a - go,
3. In His arms the chil - dren hold - ing, Long a - go, long a - go,

Words of kind - ness He was speak - ing, O so long a - go.
"Ye are of my king - dom - heav - en," O so long a - go
With His ten - der love en - fold - ing, O so long a - go.

CHORUS.

Long a - go chil - dren came, Long a - go— yet the same.

Je - sus would the chil - dren bless, Je - sus bids us come.

In the Temple.

32

FLORA KIRKLAND.

HOWARD E. SMITH.

1. In the tem - ple, in the tem - ple Stood a lit - tle boy one day,
2. It was Je - sus who was teaching, And they lis-tened to His word,
3. With the teach-ers there they found Him, Tho' a low - ly, learning youth,
4. "Let us ev - er then be loy - al To our God, and church, and home,"

And the doc - tors wondered great-ly At the words they heard Him say.
As He told them of His mis-sion From the great and might-y Lord.
But His an -swers as He told them Were complete with Bi - ble truth.
Ev - er faith-ful, ev - er trust-ing, "Nev-er mind - ing what may come."

CHORUS.

It was Je - sus! It was Je - sus! He was but a lit - tle child,

rit.

But the light of heav'n was shin-ing In His face so pure and mild.

Six Days Our Father Gives.

LIZZIE DEARMOND.

ALFRED JUDSON.

1. ¹Six days our Fa - ther gives to ²us, For work and hap - py play,
2. ¹Six days have we for all our needs, But we must ⁵rest al - way,
3. ¹Six days our Fa - ther gives to ²us, He knows just what is best,

So it would be a sin - ful thing, To steal His ³Sab bath day.
And ho - ly keep un - to the Lord, His bless - ed ³sev - enth day.
So in His love He kind - ly sends Our day of ⁶heav'n ly rest.

CHORUS.

¹Six days we call our ²own, Yes, tru - ly call our own,

But all the ho - ly ³sev-enth day Be-longs to ⁴God a - lone.

MOTIONS.—1, Hold up six fingers. 2, Lay right hand on breast. 3, Hold up index finger of right hand 4, Point up. 5, Stand erect, with hands hanging down at sides. 6, Fold arms across breast and look up.

If You Have a Pleasant Thought.

R. MORRIS.   H. R. PALMER.

1. If you have a pleas-ant thought, Sing it, sing it,
2. Ev-'ry gra-cious deed of His, Sing it, sing it,
3. Are you wea-ry, are you sad? Sing it, sing it,

As the birds sing in their sport, Sing it from the heart:
Noth-ing sounds so well as this, Sing it from the heart:
Make your-selves and oth-ers glad. Sing it from the heart:

Does the Ho-ly Spir-it move For the child-ren of His love,
How the Lord walk'd on the wave, Res-cued La-zarus from the grave,
An-gels now be-fore His face Sing of Christ's re-deem-ing grace,

Sing, and point the home a-bove, Sing it from the heart.
Died our pre-cious souls to save, Sing it from the heart.
Give the Sav-iour end-less praise, Sing it from the heart.

If You Have a Pleasant, etc.—Concluded.

CHORUS.

Sing ing, sing - ing from the heart! O the joy our songs im - part!

Je - sus, bless the tune - ful art, Sing - ing from the heart.

Holy Bible, Book Divine.

JOHN BURTON.   WM. B. BRADBURY.

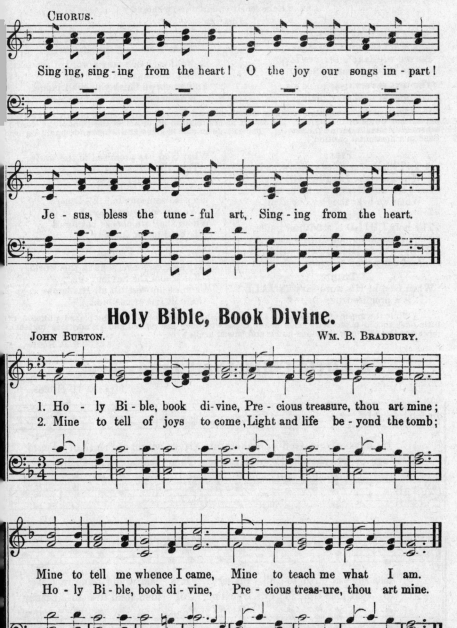

1. Ho - ly Bi - ble, book di - vine, Pre - cious treasure, thou art mine;
2. Mine to tell of joys to come, Light and life be - yond the tomb;

Mine to tell me whence I came, Mine to teach me what I am.
Ho - ly Bi - ble, book di - vine, Pre - cious treas-ure, thou art mine.

A Little Child Shall Lead Them.

(An exercise for six children and a chorus.)

LEADER.

We're only little children I know,
  Not old enough to preach;
But we will take a text we love,
  And try its lesson to teach.

The text is very dear to us all,
  It makes it so very plain;

That small as we are there's a place for us,
  When Jesus as King shall reign.

So we'll each one take a word of the text,
  And of each word we'll tell:
And when we finish you shall judge,
  Whether or no we've done well.

(Each child, as position is taken, hands the leader a card on which is plainly printed the capitalized words of the stanza. The leader places these in order across the front of the church where they remain during the service. These cards may be in green and white and should be fastened in a horizontal position.)

FIRST.

A LITTLE was all the widow had,
  Who gave the Lord her all;
Let's ask ourselves if we do as well,
  When we hear the Saviour's call.

SECOND.

The holy CHILD is a faithful guide,
  When running our earthly race;
He lived to do His Father's will,
  And daily grew in grace.

THIRD.

When God in His word says "SHALL,"
  It is a promise true;

What God has promised to the world,
  That He will surely do.

FOURTH.

We need someone to LEAD us,
  We can so easily stray;
Whom shall we choose but Jesus
  To lead us on our way?

FIFTH.

THEM means everyone in this world,
  For whom the Saviour died;
We must not rest till all His lambs
  Safe in His arms abide.

(While the music of the song, "A Little Child Shall Lead Them," is being played a number of little ones should take their places before those who have just recited and all may sing together, repeating last chorus with folded hands and bowed heads.)

—E. D. HOBBS.

A Little Child Shall Lead Them.

E. D. H.

Mrs. E. D. HOBBS.

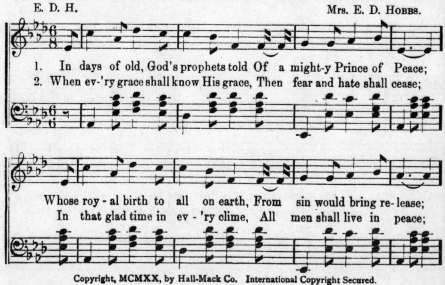

1. In days of old, God's prophets told Of a might-y Prince of Peace;
2. When ev-'ry grace shall know His grace, Then fear and hate shall cease;

Whose roy-al birth to all on earth, From sin would bring re-lease;
In that glad time in ev-'ry clime, All men shall live in peace;

REFRAIN.

A lit - tle child shall lead them, God speed the prom-ised day;

Soon may Thy king-dom come, Lord, For this we hum - bly pray.

Jesus, Tender Shepherd, Hear Me.

CLARIBEL.   Mrs. CHARLES BARNARD (Claribel.).

1. Je - sus, ten-der Shepherd, hear me; Bless Thy lit - tle lamb to-night;
2. All this day Thy hand has led me, And I thank Thee for Thy care;
3. Let my sins be all for-giv-en; Bless the friends I love so well;

Thro' the dark-ness be Thou near me, Keep me safe till morn-ing light.
Thou hast clothed me, warmed and fed me, Lis - ten to my evening pray'r!
Take me, when I die, to heav-en, Hap-py there with Thee to dwell.

No Child is Too Little.

E. D. H.

E. D. HOBBS.

1. No child is too lit-tle for Je-sus to love; His own word
2. A kind, trust-ing heart is the king-dom of love When Je-sus

tells us so. Of all the sweet things that the dear Bi-ble tells, This
comes to reign. With all who will give Him a wel-come to-day The

REFRAIN.

one is the sweet-est we know.
Sav-iour will ev-er re-main. } No child is too lit-tle for

Je-sus to love, Too lit-tle of Je-sus to learn; No child is too

lit-tle His dear love to know, Too lit-tle that love to re-turn.

The Snow Prayer.

E. E. HEWITT.　　　　　　　　　　　　　　　　　　JNO. R. SWENEY.

1. I learn'd it in the Bi-ble,　A ten-der lit-tle prayer; And when the
2. For　I have often griev'd Him With sin-ful words and ways, I'll ask Him
3. I　want to be like Je-sus,　That His pure eyes may see　A heart made

flakes are fall-ing　So beau-ti-ful and fair,　I　say to my dear Saviour
to for-give me, And help me all my days; He shed His blood so precious
clean and spot-less, To serve Him faithfully;　And　so I'll ask Him dai ly

rit.

This lit-tle pray'r I know;　"Wash me, and I shall be Whit-er than snow."
Because He lov'd me so;　"Wash me, and I shall be Whit-er than snow"
His mer-cy to be-stow;　"Wash me, and I shall be Whit-er than snow."

NOTE.—The Chorus of "Whiter Than Snow," may be sung by all after last verse.

Mission Hymn.

E. D. H.

E. D. HOBBS.

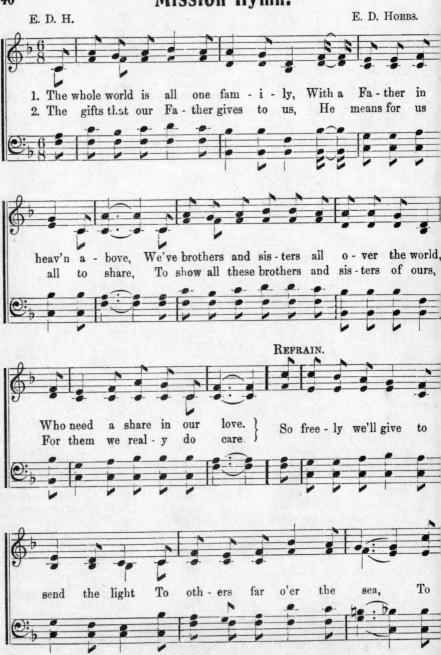

1. The whole world is all one fam - i - ly, With a Fa - ther in
2. The gifts that our Fa - ther gives to us, He means for us

heav'n a - bove, We've brothers and sis - ters all o - ver the world,
all to share, To show all these brothers and sis - ters of ours,

REFRAIN.

Who need a share in our love. } So free - ly we'll give to
For them we real - y do care. }

send the light To oth - ers far o'er the sea, To

Mission Hymn.—Concluded.

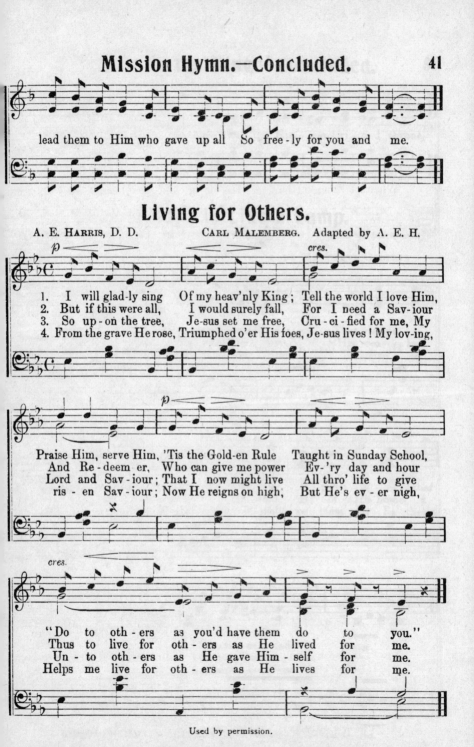

lead them to Him who gave up all So free-ly for you and me.

Living for Others.

A. E. HARRIS, D. D.   CARL MALEMBERG.   Adapted by A. E. H.

1. I will glad-ly sing   Of my heav'nly King; Tell the world I love Him,
2. But if this were all,   I would surely fall,   For I need a Sav-iour
3. So up-on the tree,   Je-sus set me free,   Cru-ci-fied for me, My
4. From the grave He rose, Triumphed o'er His foes, Je-sus lives! My lov-ing,

Praise Him, serve Him, 'Tis the Gold-en Rule   Taught in Sunday School,
And Re-deem-er,   Who can give me power   Ev-'ry day and hour
Lord and Sav-iour; That I now might live   All thro' life to give
ris-en Sav-iour; Now He reigns on high,   But He's ev-er nigh,

"Do to oth-ers   as you'd have them   do   to   you."
Thus to live for oth-ers   as He   lived   for   me.
Un-to oth-ers   as He   gave Him-self   for   me.
Helps me live for oth-ers   as He   lives   for   me.

Used by permission.

42

Jesus Hears.

(To be sung before prayer is offered.)

ELSIE DUNCAN YALE.   JOHN J. THOMAS.

1. When I speak to Him in pray'r, Je - sus hears, Je - sus hears,
2. When I would for - give-ness find, Je - sus hears, Je - sus hears,
3. When I thank Him for His love, Je - sus hears, Je - sus hears,

He is with me ev - 'ry - where, Je - sus al - ways hears.
He is ten - der, lov - ing, kind, Je - sus al - ways hears.
For His gifts from heav'n a - bove, Je - sus al - ways hears.

CHORUS.

He will hear me when I pray, He will guide me in His way,

So I'll seek Him ev - 'ry day, Je - sus al - ways hears.

Shine for Jesus.

ALICE JEAN CLEATOR. COPYRIGHT 1900, RENEWAL 1928
THE RODEHEAVER CO., OWNER
C. AUSTIN MILES.

1. In this world of darkness let us ev - er be Each a light that
2. Nev - er think your light so humble is and small That it mat - ters
3. E'en a lit - tle light can pierce the gloom a - far; It can shine for

shin-eth clear and bright; O the shin-ing ray some wand'ring soul may see,
not if it should fade; Let its radiance soft-ly thro' the dark-ness fall,
Je - sus day by day; It may serve to someone as a guid - ing star

CHORUS.

And be led to Christ the Light.
That some soul from sin be stay'd. } Shine for Je-sus! Shine for Je-sus!
That shall lead from sin a - way.

Shine for Je-sus! Shine for Je-sus!

1. 2.

Never let your light grow dim; Souls will be led to fol-low Him.

to fol-low Him.

The Song of the Book.

W. S. *(May be recited, music played.)* Rev. WM. STONE.

1. Gen - e - sis and Ex - o - dus, Le - vit - i - cus and
2. Job and Psalms and Pro - verbs and then Ec - cle - si
3. Ho - se - a and Joel, A - mos O - be - di - ah,
4. Mat - thew Mark and Luke and John, the writ - ers of the
5. First and Sec - ond Thess - a - lon - ians, First and Sec - ond

Num - bers, With Deu - ter - on - o - my com - plete the Books of law.
as - tes, With songs of Sol - o - mon are Books of po - e - try.
Jon - ah Then Mi - cah, Na - hum, Hab - ak - kuk with per - fect faith in God;
Gos - pels, The Acts, the Book of His - t'ry Ro - mans fol - low next;
Tim - othy, Then Ti - tus Phil - e - mon and He - brews, four - teen all.

Josh - ua, Judg - es, Ruth, First and Sec - ond Sam - u - el,
I - sa - iah, Jer - e - mi - ah, Lam - en - ta - tions and E - ze - ki - el,
Zeph - a - ni - ah, Hag - ga - i, *"be strong and work,"
First Cor - inth - ians, Sec - ond then Gal - a - tians and Eph - e - si - ans
Sev'n E - pis - tles, James and Pet - er One and Two

First Kings, Sec - ond Kings, Chron - i - cles One and Two; With
Dan - iel fol - lows these might - y men of God; All
Zech - a - ri - ah, Mal - a - chi last of all; And
Tell us that we must *"gird on our ar - mor" bright; Phil
John One, Two and Three, Jude, they were all with Paul; And

* Key Phrase.   Copyright, MCMXVI, by Rev. Wm. Stone.

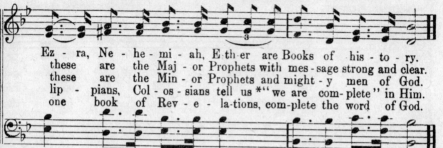

Ez - ra, Ne - he - mi - ah, E - th - er are Books of his - to - ry.
these are the Maj - or Prophets with mes - sage strong and clear.
these are the Min - or Prophets and might - y men of God.
lip - pians, Col - os - sians tell us *"we are com - plete" in Him.
one book of Rev - e - la - tions, com - plete the word of God.

Jesus Bids Us Shine.

EMILY HUNTINGTON MILLER.

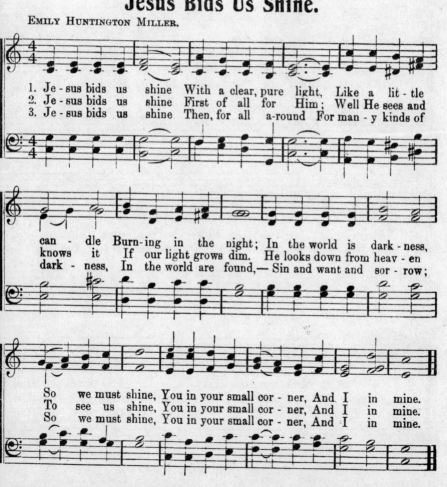

1. Je - sus bids us shine With a clear, pure light, Like a lit - tle
2. Je - sus bids us shine First of all for Him; Well He sees and
3. Je - sus bids us shine Then, for all a - round For man - y kinds of

can - dle Burn - ing in the night; In the world is dark - ness,
knows it If our light grows dim. He looks down from heav - en
dark - ness, In the world are found,— Sin and want and sor - row;

So we must shine, You in your small cor - ner, And I in mine.
To see us shine, You in your small cor - ner, And I in mine.
So we must shine, You in your small cor - ner, And I in mine.

Shine For Him.

GRACE GORDON.

HALDOR LILLENAS.

1. Shine for Him, shine for Him, Bring-ing His glad-ness and
2. Speak for Him, speak for Him, Tell of the won-der-ful
3. Live for Him, live for Him, Live ev-'ry day for the

cheer, Each lit-tle child may be His lit-tle light,
King, Each lit-tle child may His mes-sen-ger be,
King, Each lit-tle child Je-sus' bid-ding may do,

Gleam-ing so stead-i-ly, gleam-ing so bright, Just like a
Tell-ing of love that is change-less and free, Love of the
Serve Him with love that is faith-ful and true, Do-ing just

can-dle in dark-ness of night, Shine for Him, shine for Him.
Fa-ther for you and for me, Speak for Him, speak for Him.
what He would have you to do, Live for Him, live for Him.

All His Works Praise Him.

(Before the first verse is sung the teacher fastens several stars cut from gilt paper upon the wall. Before the second verse, a silver crescent, to represent the moon. Before the third verse, a gilt circle, to suggest the sun.)

GRACE GORDON.

HALDOR LILLENAS.

1. Lit - tle stars that shine so fair, With your gold - en rays,
2. Sil - ver moon in dis - tant sky, 'Mid the star - ry ways,
3. Gold - en sun that gleams so bright, Thro' our hap - py days,

O tell your heav'nly Fa-ther's love, The King Cre-a - tor praise.
O tell of God who reigns a-bove, The King Cre-a - tor praise.
O tell of Him the Lord of light, The great Cre-a - tor praise.

CHORUS.

All His works shall praise Him, All His works so fair,

Lo, their bright glory is tell-ing the sto-ry, A Fa - ther's care. . . .

Sunbeams of Love.

FRONA SCOTT.   HALDOR LILLENAS.

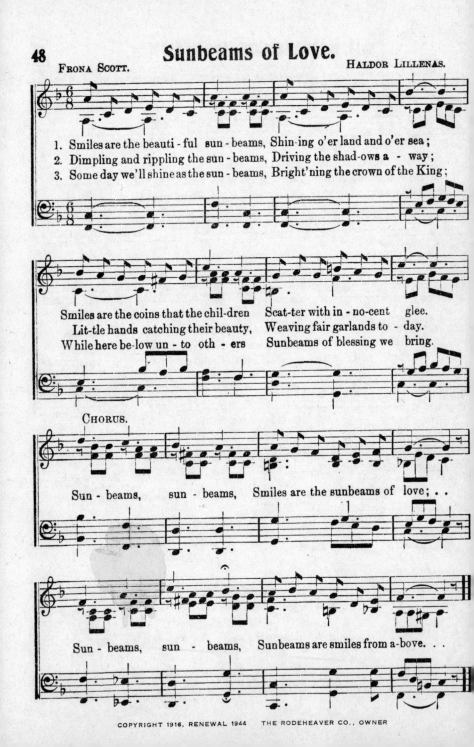

1. Smiles are the beauti - ful sun - beams, Shin-ing o'er land and o'er sea;
2. Dimpling and rippling the sun - beams, Driving the shad-ows a - way;
3. Some day we'll shine as the sun - beams, Bright'ning the crown of the King;

Smiles are the coins that the chil-dren   Scat-ter with in - no-cent   glee.
Lit-tle hands catching their beauty,   Weaving fair garlands to - day.
While here be-low un - to oth - ers   Sunbeams of blessing we   bring.

CHORUS.

Sun - beams,   sun - beams,   Smiles are the sunbeams of love; . . .

Sun - beams,   sun - beams,   Sunbeams are smiles from a-bove. . .

God's Gifts.

(As the first verse is sung, a miniature sheaf of wheat or other grain should be placed on the table or desk. During the singing of the second verse, place a basket of fruit. As the third verse is sung, a large cardboard heart lettered "Gratitude" should be fastened upon the wall. This song may be appropriately used as a programme number for a Harvest Festival.)

GRACE GORDON.   GRACE L. HOSMER.

1. Won-der-ful gifts from heav'n a-bove. Praise, O praise the Fa - ther!
2. Boun-ti-ful har-vest fills the field, Praise, O praise the Fa - ther!
3. Sweet-est of songs to Him we sing, Praise, O praise the Fa - ther!

Tok-ens of kind-ness, care, and love, Praise, O praise the Fa - ther!
Un-to our King our thanks we yield, Praise, O praise the Fa - ther!
Grate-ful the hearts to Him we bring, Praise, O praise the Fa - ther!

Thro' the sun-shine and the rain He has watch'd the hill and plain,
Fruit up-on the bend-ing tree, Neath the sun-ny skies we see,
From His roy-al heav'n-ly throne, Gifts He gives un-to His own,

He has giv'n the gold-en grain, Praise, O praise the Fa - ther!
To the Giv-er thanks should be, Praise, O praise the Fa - ther!
Praise is His, and His a-lone, Praise, O praise the Fa - ther!

I Belong to the King.

IDA L. REED.
SOLO OR DUET.

MAURICE A. CLIFTON.

1. I be-long to the King, I'm a child of His love, I shall
2. I be-long to the King, and He loves me I know, For His
3. I be-long to the King, and His prom-ise is sure, That we

dwell in His pal-ace so fair; For He tells of its bliss in yon
mer-cy and kindness so free, Are un-ceas-ing-ly mine, wher-so-
all shall be gathered at last In His kingdom a-bove, by life's

heav-en a-bove, And His chil-dren its splen-dors shall share.
ev-er I go, And my ref-uge un-fail-ing is He.
wa-ters so pure, When this life with its tri-als is past.

CHORUS.

I be-long to the King, I'm a child of His love, And He
nev-er for-sak-eth His own; He will call me some day to His

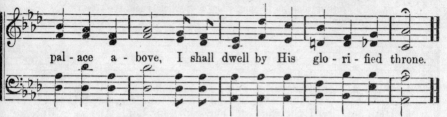

pal - ace a - bove, I shall dwell by His glo - ri - fied throne.

God's Word is Like a Lamp.

(Before this is sung the teacher may either draw a lamp in yellow crayon on the blackboard, or, better still, place an open Bible on a table, and beside it a lighted candle.)

GRACE GORDON.   ELLA MATTHEWS GODFREY.

1. God's word is like a lamp di - vine, That gleams a-
2. It tells us of His ten - der love, His cease - less
3. It tells us that our Sav - iour came To live on

far with gold - en rays, And for its prom - is - es that
care, His won - drous might, It tells us of His home a-
earth our lov - ing Lord, And so we bless our Fa - ther's

shine, His ho - ly name we glad - ly praise. . . .
bove, Where all is joy and all is light. . . . .
name, For like a lamp is His own word. . . . .

We Welcome You.

(Greeting song, to be sung when new scholars join the class.)

GRACE GORDON.   GRACE L. HOSMER.

Grazioso.

1. With a greet-ing true we would wel-come you With our hap-py
2. Here we come to sing to our Sav-iour King, Joy-ful songs of
3. Here we read the word of our lov-ing Lord, And we lift our

songs of cheer, Yes, a wel-come kind you will ev-er find,
grate-ful praise, And we know He's near, and will ev-er hear,
hearts in prayer, Then the sto-ry sweet how we oft re-peat,

CHORUS.

In the school we love so dear. }
Hap-py songs His children raise. } Wel-come sing, wel-come sing,
Of a Fa-ther's ten-der care. }

Hap-py greet-ing kind and true, welcome we would give to you.

My Shepherd.

(Before this hymn is sung the 23d Psalm may be repeated.)

GRACE GORDON.

ELLA MATTHEWS GODFREY.

Andantino. p

1. My Sav-iour is my shep-herd, So ten-der and so kind,
2. My Sav-iour is my shep-herd, And O how strong His arm,
3. My Sav-iour is my shep-herd, And O He loves me so,

And if I wan-der from His side, He seeks and He will find.
To keep and hold and shel-ter me, To shield me from all harm.
He guides me to the pas-tures fair, Where living wa - ters flow.

Like lambs are lit - tle chil - dren, With - in His word we read,
He calls the lit - tle chil - dren, He guides to pas-tures fair,
With - in His arms He gath - ers The lambs so ten - der - ly,

molto rit. e dim.

My Sav-iour is my shep-herd, And I'll go where He may lead.
My Sav-iour is my shep-herd, And I'll trust His ten - der care.
My Sav-iour is my shep-herd, And I know He'll care for me.

The Cheerful Giver.

(To be suug while the collection is being taken)

GRACE GORDON.   GRACE L. HOSMER.

1. God loves a cheer-ful giv - er,   Iu His own word we read,
2. For help that's glad-ly giv - en,   E'en to the low-liest one,
3. God loves a cheer-ful giv - er,   So we our gifts would bring,

So we'll re-mem-ber ev - er,   To give to those in need.
Will please our Lord in heav - en, For un - to Him 'tis done.
And we'll for-get, no, nev - er, Our lov - ing Lord and King.

CHORUS.

We're giv - ers,   glad giv - ers   For love of our dear Lord;

We're giv - ers,   glad giv - ers,   We heed His bless - ed word.

The Captain's Call.

55

(Song especially for Primary boys. Before this is sung the notes of the reveille may be played on the piano.)

GRACE GORDON.

GRACE L. HOSMER.

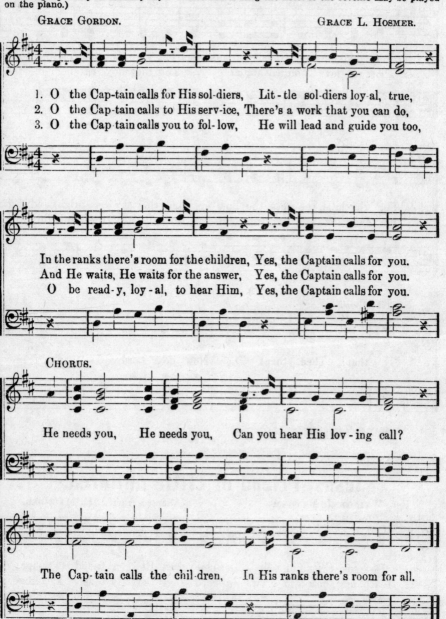

1. O the Cap-tain calls for His sol-diers, Lit-tle sol-diers loy-al, true,
2. O the Cap-tain calls to His serv-ice, There's a work that you can do,
3. O the Cap-tain calls you to fol-low, He will lead and guide you too,

In the ranks there's room for the children, Yes, the Captain calls for you.
And He waits, He waits for the answer, Yes, the Captain calls for you.
O be read-y, loy-al, to hear Him, Yes, the Captain calls for you.

CHORUS.

He needs you, He needs you, Can you hear His lov-ing call?

The Cap-tain calls the chil-dren, In His ranks there's room for all.

Hymn of Thanks.

C. F. O.

ALFRED JUDSON.

1. For my home and friends I thank Thee, For my fa - ther, moth-er, dear,
2. Those I love Thou wilt watch o - ver, Tho' they may be far a - way,

For the hills, the trees, the flow - ers, And the sky so bright and clear.
For Thou lov - est lit - tle chil-dren, And wilt hear the words they say.

REFRAIN.

* I thank Thee, thank Thee, Now, dear Lord, I thank Thee.

* Clasp hands in attitude of prayer.

Jesus, Friend of Little Children.

Rev. WALTER J. MATHAMS.

Adapted from J. H. MAUNDER.

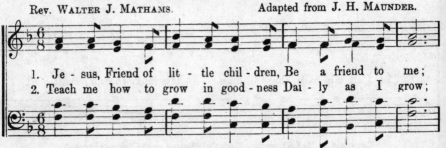

1. Je - sus, Friend of lit - tle chil - dren, Be a friend to me;
2. Teach me how to grow in good - ness Dai - ly as I grow;

Take my hand and ev - er keep me Close to Thee.
Thou hast been a child, and sure - ly Thou dost know.

Sabbath Morning Bells.

Mrs. C. G. Goodwin.   Bradbury's "Golden Shower," 1862.

Ho - ly Sab - bath, hap - py morn-ing, Joy - ful - ly the bells we hear,

Sweet - ly call - ing, gent - ly call - ing Us to praise and prayer.

Sweet-ly sound-ing thro' each street, And float-ing on the qui - et air,

Comes the dear, fa - mil - iar greet-ing, Call - ing us to prayer.

O Little Lad of Nazareth.

(Before this is sung a map of Palestine should be hung up before the class, and a gold star fastened upon Nazareth. Beside it should be placed a print of Hofman's picture, "Christ at the age of Twelve.")

ELSIE DUNCAN YALE.   GRACE L. HOSMER.

1. O lit-tle lad of Naz-a-reth, Who liv'd in days of old,
2. O lit-tle lad of Naz-a-reth, O-be-dient, lov-ing, true,
3. O lit-tle lad of Naz-a-reth, Who liv'd in low-ly home,

We may not walk and talk with Thee, Nor yet Thy face be-hold.
O make us more and more like Thee, Thy bless-ed will to do.
With joy-ous songs of hap-py praise, To Thee the chil-dren come.

REFRAIN.

And still with love we would seek Thee, Thy lit-tle friends we would be,

And this we pray in work or play, O make us more like Thee.

The Mountains. 59

(This song may be used in connection with a sand table. Let the children make—with the sand—a representation of Jerusalem, surrounded by hills. Just before singing repeat Psalm 125 : 2.)

GRACE GORDON.   HALDOR LILLENAS.

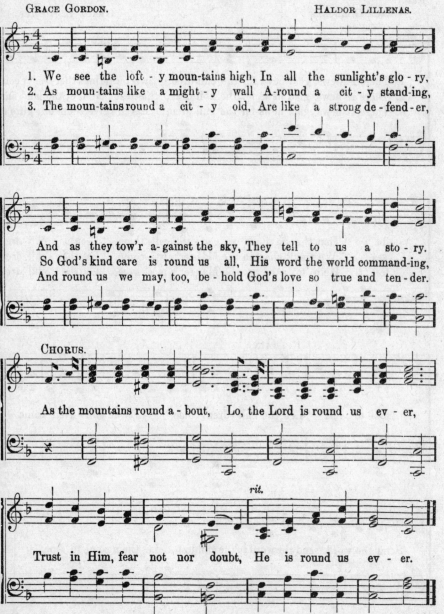

1. We see the loft - y moun-tains high, In all the sunlight's glo - ry,
2. As moun-tains like a might - y wall A-round a cit - y stand-ing,
3. The moun-tains round a cit - y old, Are like a strong de - fend - er,

And as they tow'r a-gainst the sky, They tell to us a sto - ry.
So God's kind care is round us all, His word the world command-ing,
And round us we may, too, be - hold God's love so true and ten - der.

CHORUS.

As the mountains round a - bout, Lo, the Lord is round us ev - er,

rit.

Trust in Him, fear not nor doubt, He is round us ev - er.

News for the Children.

(This may be used as a Missionary Song, and sung just before a collection for Foreign Missions is taken. A missionary map, or better still, a missionary poster should be displayed before the class.)

GRACE GORDON.   GRACE L. HOSMER.

1. There is news, glad news for the chil-dren, Sweeter tidings there ne'er could be, That the Sav-iour so gen-tly calls them, "Let the chil-dren come to me."
2. There is news, glad news for the chil-dren, Speed it far o'er the land and sea, We would share in the Mas-ter's wel-come, "Let the chil-dren come to me."
3. There is news, glad news for the chil-dren, May we give them our gifts so free, Help to car-ry the Mas-ter's mes-sage, "Let the chil-dren come to me."

REFRAIN

Let the chil-dren come, Let the chil-dren come, Send the word, send the word to the children, Let them come to me.

By the Shores of Galilee.

(Before this is sung the story of the call of the first disciples may be read or told.)

GRACE GORDON.   GRACE L. HOSMER.

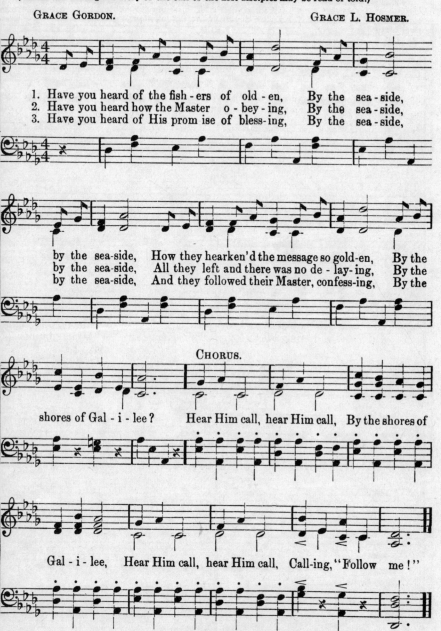

1. Have you heard of the fish-ers of old-en, By the sea-side, by the sea-side, How they hearken'd the message so gold-en, By the shores of Gal-i-lee?

2. Have you heard how the Master o-bey-ing, By the sea-side, by the sea-side, All they left and there was no de-lay-ing, By the shores of Gal-i-lee?

3. Have you heard of His prom-ise of bless-ing, By the sea-side, by the sea-side, And they followed their Master, confess-ing, By the shores of Gal-i-lee?

CHORUS.

Hear Him call, hear Him call, By the shores of Gal-i-lee, Hear Him call, hear Him call, Call-ing, "Follow me!"

62 If Jesus Comes Into Your Heart.

(This may be used in connection with a blackboard lesson. Draw an outline of a heart up the board, and as the first verse is sung letter "JOY" within the outline. As the second verse sung, letter "LOVE," and during the singing of the Chorus after the second verse letter beneath the heart "JESUS.")

GRACE GORDON.　　　　　　　　　　　　GRACE L. HOSMER.

1. If Je-sus comes in-to your heart to stay, He brings to you
2. If Je-sus comes in-to your heart to stay, He brings to you

joy like a sun-beam's ray, Like sun-beams so bright, He
love that will last for aye, The love of the King Such

gives you His light, And keeps and guards you by day and night.
glad-ness will bring That songs of prais-es to Him you'll sing.

CHORUS.

Hark! Hark! Hear His call! Hark! Hark! One and all, Hear His

voice and His word o-bey, He will come in your heart to stay.

I'm Glad. I've Come to Sunday School.

C. H. M. (The Glad Song.) CHARLES H. MASKEL.

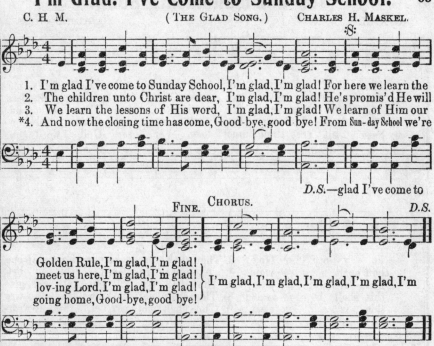

1. I'm glad I've come to Sunday School, I'm glad, I'm glad! For here we learn the
2. The children unto Christ are dear, I'm glad, I'm glad! He's promis'd He will
3. We learn the lessons of His word, I'm glad, I'm glad! We learn of Him our
*4. And now the closing time has come, Good-bye, good-bye! From Sun-day School we're

D.S.—glad I've come to

FINE. CHORUS. D.S.

Golden Rule, I'm glad, I'm glad!
meet us here, I'm glad, I'm glad!
lov-ing Lord, I'm glad, I'm glad!
going home, Good-bye, good-bye!
} I'm glad, I'm glad, I'm glad, I'm glad, I'm

Sunday School, I'm glad, I'm glad.

* Fourth verse may be omitted, when not used for a closing hymn.

Good-Bye Hymn.

Hymnal Companion.

O Lord, our hearts would give Thee praise, Ere now our school we   end,—

For this Thy day,   the best   of   days,   Je-sus, the children's Friend.

Ten Commandments Song.

C. A. M.

C. Austin Miles.

1. Thou shalt not have, so says the Lord, Be - fore me
3. Thou shalt not take my name in vain, Else guilt - less
5. Thy fa - ther and thy moth - er, too, Thou shalt do
7. To base de - sire thou shalt not yield, God's word on
9. False wit - ness thou must nev - er bear, God's word on

an - y oth - er God; 2. Thou shalt not make nor wor - ship one,
thou shalt not re - main; 4. Al - ways re - mem - ber, this o - bey,
hon - or and be true; 6. Thou shalt not kill, but rath - er give
this shall be re - vealed; 8. Thou shalt not steal nor take a - way
this is ver - y clear; 10. Thou shalt not cov - et, this is wrong,

CHORUS.

I am thy God and I a - lone.
Ho - ly to keep the Sab - bath day.
Out of thy love that all may live.   } Ten Com - mand - ments
That which is not thine own al - way.
If to an - oth - er it be - long.

sent from heav'n, God to me each one has giv'n;

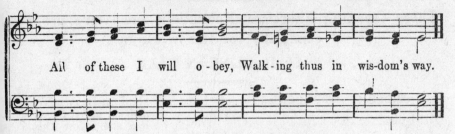

All of these I will o-bey, Walk-ing thus in wis-dom's way.

The Ten Commandments.

NOTE.—Two Commandments should be read (or recited in concert,) then sing the correspond-ing stanzas, as numbered.

And God spoke all these words, saying:

I. Thou shalt have no other gods before me.

II. Thou shalt not make unto thee any graven image, or any likeness of any thing that is in heaven above, or that is in the earth beneath, or that is in the water under the earth; thou shalt not bow down thyself to them, nor serve them; for I the Lord thy God am a jealous God, visiting the iniquity of the fathers upon the children unto the third and fourth generation of them that hate me; and showing mercy unto thousands of them that love me, and keep my com-mandments.

III. Thou shalt not take the name of the Lord thy God in vain; for the Lord will not hold him guiltless that taketh his name in vain.

IV. Remember the Sabbath day, to keep it holy. Six days shalt thou labor, and do all thy work; but the seventh day is the Sab-bath of the Lord thy God; in it thou shalt not do any work, thou, nor thy son, nor thy daughter, thy man servant, nor thy maid servant, nor thy cattle, nor thy stranger that is within thy gates; for in six days the Lord made heaven and earth, the sea, and all that in them is, and rested the seventh day: wherefore the Lord blessed the Sabbath day, and hallowed it.

V. Honor thy father and thy mother: that thy days may be long upon the land which the Lord thy God giveth thee.

VI. Thou shalt not kill.

VII. Thou shalt not commit adultery.

VIII. Thou shalt not steal.

IX. Thou shalt not bear false witness against thy neighbor.

X. Thou shalt not covet thy neighbor's house, thou shalt not covet thy neighbor's wife, nor his man servant, nor his maid ser-vant, nor his ox, nor his ass, nor any thing that is thy neighbor's.

—*Ex. 20 : 1–17.*

Gloria Patri.

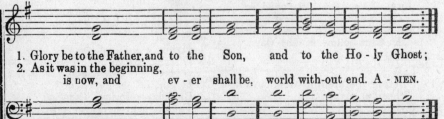

1. Glory be to the Father, and to the Son, and to the Ho-ly Ghost;
2. As it was in the beginning,
   is now, and ev-er shall be, world with-out end. A - MEN.

These Opening Exercises, Recitations, etc., were prepared especially for this work by
ELSIE DUNCAN YALE

ORDER OF SERVICE No. 1

1. Hymn.
2. All:

Welcome, happy welcome here
To the school we love so dear,
Where our joyous songs are heard
Where we learn from God's own
word.

3. Prayer:

Jesus, Friend of little children,
Bless us as we meet Thee here,
Though our eyes may not behold
Thee,
Yet we know that Thou art near.

4. Repeat Beatitudes.
5. Hymn.
6. *Teacher*—What does Jesus tell us of
Himself?

Class or individual scholars:
"I am the good Shepherd, the Good
Shepherd giveth His life for the
sheep."
"I am the Light of the World. He
that followeth me shall not walk
in darkness, but shall have the
light of life."
"I am the Door. By Me if any man
enter in, He shall go in and out
and find pasture."
"I am the Bread of Life."
"I am the Resurrection and the
Life."

7. Prayer:

Jesus, Friend of little children,
Guide and guard us every day,
Help us as we try to serve Thee,
Help us follow in Thy way.

8. Hymn.
9. Lesson.
10. Offering. Repeat, "God loveth a
cheerful giver."
11. Hymn.
12. Birthday Offering.

Saviour, hear our birthday prayer,

Keep, O keep him (her) in Thy care,
And through all the years to be,
May he love and follow Thee.

13. Hymn.

ORDER OF SERVICE No. 2

1. Hymn.
2. Repeat:

On God's holy day so blest,
Day of worship, day of rest,
We have come His praise to sing,
Learn of Him the heavenly King.

3. Lord's prayer.
4. *Teacher*—What is God's commandment about His day?

Class—"Remember the Sabbath day
to keep it holy." Ex. 20:8.
Teacher—What does God say about
His house?
Class—"My house shall be called a
house of prayer for all nations."
Teacher—What does God say of His
word?
Class—"Heaven and earth shall pass
away, but My word shall not pass
away." Matt. 24:35.
Teacher—What will the study of
God's word do for us?
Class—"The entrance of Thy word
giveth light."

5. Hymn.
6. Repeat: Books of Bible.
7. Prayer:

Father, let thy word divine,
Like a light upon us shine,
May it in our hearts abide,
May it ever be our guide.

8. Lesson.
9. Hymn.
10. Offering. Repeat: "Freely ye have
received, freely give."
11. Hymn.
12. Birthday offering. Repeat:

Father, hear us as we pray,
Bless and guide him (her) day by
day,

May Thy light upon him (her) shine,
Keep him (her) in Thy care divine.
13. Closing hymn.

ORDER OF OPENING SERVICE FOR A RAINY SUNDAY

This should be made an especially cheerful service. A vase of flowers should be upon the desk, and if it is not possible to procure natural flowers, crepe paper daffodils may be substituted with pleasing effect. It may be well to give special reward cards to children who are present on a rainy day.

1. Hymn.
2. Repeat:
Though the skies are dull and gray,
Though it is a rainy day,
In our hearts with light divine,
Will the love of Jesus shine.
3. Prayer:
Jesus, send Thy heavenly light,
Fill our hearts with sunshine bright,
So we evermore may be,
Little sunbeams, Lord for Thee.
4. Hymn.
5. *Teacher*—Who sends the rain?
Answer—"Let us fear the Lord our God that giveth rain both the former and the latter in His season." Jer. 5:24.
Teacher—How does God compare Himself to rain?
Answer—"He shall come down upon the mown grass like showers that water the earth." Ps. 72:6.
Teacher—How does God compare His Word to rain?
Answer—"For as the rain cometh down and the snow from Heaven, and returneth not but watereth the earth, and maketh it bring forth and bud that it may give seed to the sower and bread to the eater, so shall my word be that goeth forth out of my mouth; it shall not return unto me void, but it shall accomplish that which I please, it shall prosper in the thing whereunto I sent it." Isa. 55:10, 11.
Teacher—What does God promise the rain will do for us?
Answer—"Then will I give you rain in due season and the land shall yield her increase, and the trees of the field shall yield their fruit." Lev. 26:6.
6. Teacher tells story of Elijah on Mt. Carmel and the rain sent in answer to prayer.
7. Hymn.
8. Prayer.
For refreshing silv'ry rain,
Falling o'er the field and plain,
Rain that wakes to life the seed,
Rain that buds and blossoms need,
Rain that helps a harvest to bring,
We thank our heavenly King.

OPENING SERVICE FOR SNOWY SUNDAY

1. Hymn.
2. Repeat:
See the snowflakes white and fair,
Falling through the frosty air,
On the field and on the town,
Slowly, slowly drifting down.
3. Prayer:
Like the snowflakes pure and white,
Jesus, keep us in Thy sight,
Fair and spotless would we be,
Make us, Jesus, more like Thee.
4. Hymn.
5. *Teacher*—What does the Bible say about the snow?
"He saith to the snow, Be thou on the earth." Job 37:6.
"Hast thou entered into the treasures of the snow or hast thou seen the treasures of the hail?" Job 38:22.
"He giveth the snow like wool, He scattereth the hoarfrost like ashes." Psalms 147:16.
"Wash me and I shall be whiter than snow." Psa. 51:6.
"Though your sins be as scarlet, they shall be as white as snow." Isa. 18.
6. Hymn No. 39.
7. Prayer:
For the snow that falls so light,
Covering earth with mantle white,
Keeping buds and blossoms warm,
Shelt'ring them from wintry harm,
For the lovely snow we see,
Father, we give thanks to Thee.

PRIMARY PROMOTION EXERCISE

The promotion of primary children to the junior class should be made a "special occasion," and recognition given of the work which has been done. Decorate the platform prettily, banking it with ferns and potted plants, placing the lower in the centre and the higher at the sides. If space will permit, a pretty plan is to make an arch in the centre of the platform which can be done as follows: Fasten to the floor by means of uprights four slender props—clothes props sawed off to the desired height will serve the purpose satisfactorily. Over these stretch mesh wire fencing about a foot in width, and twine the meshes with greenery and flowers. From each side of the arch extend a rope of green to the side of the platform. The "graduates" enter singing a processional and take their places on the platform back of the arch.

1. Brief introduction by superintendent or teacher.
2. Lord's Prayer by all.
3. Hymn (selected), Class.
4. *Superintendent*—What names have we for the Bible? Answer—God's Word, the Scriptures.
5. *Superintendent* — Why should we study the Bible? Class repeats selected verses.
6. *Superintendent*—What does the Bible teach us of God? Class repeats selected verses.
7. Hymn. Blessed Bible.
8. *Superintendent* — What have we learned of Jesus? The story of the life of Christ should be told by six scholars: (1) His birth; (2) Childhood; (3) His works; (4) His trial and crucifixion; (5) His resurrection; (6) His ascension.
9. Hymn.
10. Bible drill—call for verses by chapter and verse, as, for example, John 3:16.
11. *Superintendent*—Whom does Jesus say are blessed? Repeat Beatitudes.
12. *Superintendent*—What invitation has He given the children? Repeat Luke 18:16.
13. Presentation of diplomas.
14. Junior boy or girl.

We welcome you, we welcome you to this dear class of ours,
And may you ever faithful be in sunshine or in showers;
Of Jesus we would ever learn, we strive to walk His way,
And so we gladly welcome you on this Promotion Day.
Led by a junior girl and boy the class marches through arch, the junior class comes upon platform and all join in hymn.

MISSIONARY DIALOGUE

One or more children should be costumed in foreign style (Chinese, Japanese, Hindoo, etc.). The question verse should be asked by one person, the reply by the children representing foreign countries.

Little children come today,
From the land so far away,
What have you to tell us, pray,
Eager little children?

We have come from lands of night,
Where they have no gospel light,
Where they have no joy so bright.
Help the little children.

Have you never, never heard
Of the kind and loving Lord;
Have you never read His word,
Eager little children?

We have heard there is a King,
One whose praise the children sing,
Haste the happy news to bring,
Help the little children.

ALL
Give, O give with gladness,
Help to tell His love,
Help to tell the story
Of the King above.

Send the joyous message,
To the land of night;
Send to little children,
Blessed gospel light!

THE BLESSED BIBLE

There's a light to guide our way,
Leading onward every day,
Shining with a golden ray,
    'Tis the blessed Bible.
There is bread from Heaven indeed,
Bread on which our soul may feed,
Living bread for every need,
    'Tis the blessed Bible.

There's a sword of power and might,
For the battle of the right,
It will conquer in the fight,
    'Tis the blessed Bible.
There's a staff so tried and true,
Daily strength it will renew,
It will help us safely through,
    'Tis the blessed Bible.

THE LITTLE SEED

Just a seed, a tiny seed,
    Which we plant with care,
See we place it in the ground,
    Then we leave it there.

Just a plant, a pretty plant,
    And we know 'tis true,
That from just a tiny seed,
    Day by day it grew.

Just a deed, a kindly deed,
    Though it may seem small,
Yet may blossom like a flower
    For the Lord of all.

Ev'ry little kindly deed
Is just like a tiny seed,
May we sow as best we may
Seeds of kindness every day.

After reciting the first verse, a child may carefully plant a seed in a small flower-pot. After the second verse a plant should be placed on a table or stand. After the third verse, a child should place flowers in a vase.

THE PROMISES

Provide a number of gilt stars at least one for each member of the class. After each verse the children may repeat Bible promises, each one who repeats a promise being permitted to fasten a star on the wall.

Just like golden stars that shine,
Are God's promises divine;
    Let us hear and heed them,
Promises of tender love,
Promises from God above,
    All our life we need them!

Just like golden stars so bright,
Cheering with their wondrous light,
    Are the words of olden.
Precious promises so true,
Meant for me and meant for you,
    Words of life so golden.

Just like stars in Heaven above,
Are the wondrous words of love,
    In God's word we read them.
Blessed truth that will impart,
Happiness to every heart,
    Let us hear and heed them.

Promises so wondrous sweet,
O'er and o'er would we repeat,
Like the golden stars that shine,
Promises of love divine.

CHILDREN IN THE TEMPLE

Dialogue. This may be given by one child and class, or the class may be divided into two groups—one group asking the question, and the other giving the answer.

Why sing, O ye children, your songs of
    rejoicing?
    Through courts of the temple your
    carols ring clear.
Our praise to our Saviour we gladly are
    voicing,
    We greet our Redeemer, behold He
    is here!

Why echo hosannas through all the
    courts ringing,
    Who is it ye herald with jubilant
    song?
Our praise unto Jesus we gladly are
    bringing,
    For He is the Saviour expected so
    long.

And will He receive you, who come
    now confessing,
    If King of the Heaven and Ruler is
    He?

The children may ever receive His kind
 blessing,
His message we harkened, "O come
 unto me."

THE ARMOR OF GOD

*Object Lesson. For this the teacher
will need helmet, sword, shield, sandals
cut in outline from silver paper. After
each verse the piece of armor described
should be fastened upon the wall or
blackboard.*

There's a shining armor,
 Given by our King;
Lo, the Bible is our sword,
 Victory to bring.

Faith so strong and steady,
 Trusting, Lord, in thee,
Faith that holds a Father fast,
 This our shield shall be.

Take salvation's helmet,
 Mighty 'tis, and strong;
It will ever keep from harm,
 Fighting 'gainst the wrong.

Peace shall be like sandals,
 Helping on our way;
Peace that God the Father gives,
 When we e'er obey.

ALL RECITE
Armor so wonderful,
 Armor of might,
Help us win victory,
 Battling for right.

LITTLE CAPTIVE MAIDEN

*Dialogue for two little girls or for
little girl and class.*

Little captive maiden,
 In a land afar,
Do you for Judea long,
 Where your kindred are?

Yes, I'm often lonely,
 But I kneel in prayer,
And the Lord I trust and love,
 Keeps me in His care.

Do you seek to serve Him,
 Though afar from home,

Pointing to the Lord of all,
 Bidding others come?

Naaman, the leper,
 Was my master kind,
And I bade him with the Lord
 Help and healing find.

Did your Syrian Master
 Haste with eager soul,
Seek the Lord you love and serve,
 That he might be whole?

Yes, he sought with gladness,
 God I serve and love,
And his leprosy was cleansed
 By the King above.
ALL
So a little child may speak,
 Kindly helpful word,
Pointing others in the way,
 To the loving Lord.

TRUST HIS CARE

*A dialogue. The child personating a
flower should wear white with a pink
sash and hair bow and should carry
flowers. The one representing a bird
wears blue sash and hairbow, and as she
recites the verse assigned, makes flying
motions with arms. The child representing a star may wear white with yellow
sash and hairbow, crown of gilt cardboard, and carry wand tipped with gilt
star. Of course, this special costuming
is only necessary when this is given as a
"special day" program number.*

Little flower so bright and gay,
 Little flower so fair,
Have you come to tell us here,
Message sweet and message dear,
 Of a Father's care?

This the message of the flowers,
In the happy summer hours,
Blooming 'neath the skies above,
 Trust ye in His love.

Little bird with joyous wing,
 Little bird of air,
Merrily we hear you sing,
Do you happy tidings bring,
 Of a Father's care?

This the message of the bird
Ringing far and near 'tis heard,
Ringing 'neath the skies above,
Trust ye in His love.

Little star that shines on high
    Message do you bear,
Shining in the sky so bright,
Do you tell us by your light
    Of a Father's care?

This the message of the star
Shining near and shining far,
Whispering from the skies above,
Trust ye in His love.

ALL

Trust His love and trust His care,
Every day and everywhere.

BIBLE CHILDREN

1. What little child was hidden in an ark of bulrushes? Moses.
2. What little child was dedicated to temple service? Samuel.
3. What little girl showed her master how to find a cure for his leprosy? Naaman's maid.
4. What did the little lad give to Jesus to help feed the multitude? Five loaves and two fishes.
5. What little girl was raised from the dead by Jesus? The daughter of Jairus.
6. What boy wore a coat of many colors? Joseph.
7. What did Jesus say to the children brought by their mothers? "Suffer the little children to come unto me and forbid them not, for of such is the kingdom of heaven."
8. Where did the children sing hosannas to Jesus? In the temple.
9. What is said of Jesus' childhood? "And Jesus increased in wisdom and in stature and in favor with God and man." Luke 2:52.
10. What does Jesus say of child-like humility? "Except ye be converted and become as little children, ye shall not enter into the kingdom of heaven." Matt. 18:3.

THE PARABLES' OBJECT LESSON

Instead of the objects mentioned in the following lesson, pictures may be used if preferred. If it is desired to lengthen the lesson, the parables may be told by different members of the class.

1. What is a parable? An earthly story with a heavenly meaning.
2. What parable does this represent (holds up a toy sheep)? The Ninety and Nine.
3. What parable does this represent (holds up seeds)? The Sower.
4. Wheat—The parable of the wheat and tares.
5. Grapes—The vineyard and the king's son.
6. Piece of silver—The woman and the lost piece of silver.
7. Ten pieces of silver—The talents.
8. Lamp—The ten virgins.
9. Pearl (bead may be used)—The pearl of great price.
10. Net—The net and fishes.

OBJECT LESSON ON THE LIFE OF CHRIST

Instead of the objects themselves, the teacher may use pictures, but the former are preferable. Instead of repeating the verses indicated, different children may tell the story in their own words.

Teacher holding up miniature shepherd's crook. "How does a shepherd remind us of Jesus?"
Class repeats Luke 2:8, 9, 10, 11.
Teacher holds up star cut from silver cardboard.
Class repeats Matt. 2:2.
Teacher holds up plane or hammer.
Class repeats Matt. 13:55.
Teacher holds dove cut from cardboard.
Class repeats Matt. 3:16, 17.
Teacher holds up cross.
Class repeats Luke 23:33.
Teacher holds up crown.
Class repeats Matt. 28:5, 6.
Music selected from this book may be used in connection with the exercise, if desired.

LIGHT OF THE WORLD

Object Lesson

For this purpose provide either a square board two inches thick, in which holes are bored to hold tiny candles, or a square pan filled with sand. In the latter case surround the edge of the pan with moss or vines. If desired the sand may be molded to suggest a relief map with bits of mirror for ocean and lakes. Provide very small white tapers and one white candle. The twelve tapers should be lit from the candle, and the other tapers from these twelve and so on.

Teacher—Who is the Light of the world?

Class—Jesus said, "I am the Light of the World. He that followeth Me shall not walk in darkness, but shall have the light of life."

Teacher lights large candle, places it in centre of board or sand.

Teacher—How was the light spread?

Class—Jesus called twelve men to be disciples, and sent them forth to teach and to preach.

Teacher—Who were these twelve men?

Class names twelve apostles and as each is named teacher lights a taper, placing them in a circle around the candle.

Teacher—How was the light of the gospel still further spread?

Class—Many others believed in Jesus and in turn became teachers and preachers of the word.

Teacher lights a number of other tapers and places them in sand or upon board.

Teacher—How may we help to send the light?

Class—Let your light so shine before men that they may see your good works and glorify your Father which is in Heaven.

MOTHER'S DAY

1. What mother gave her little son to the service of God in the temple? Hannah.
2. What mother was engaged by a princess to take care of her own baby? The mother of Moses.
3. What mother was driven out into the desert with her son? Hagar.
4. Whose son was raised from the dead by Jesus? The son of the widow of Nain.
5. What mother asked of Christ that her two sons sit one on His right hand and the other on His left in His Kingdom? The mother of James and John.
6. How does God compare His love to that of a mother? "As one whom his mother comforteth, so will I comfort you." Isa. 66:13.
7. To whom did Jesus entrust his Mother as He was dying upon the cross? John.
8. What did Jesus say when mothers brought their children to Him? "Suffer the little children to come unto Me and forbid them not, for of such is the Kingdom of Heaven."
9. What does Jesus say about mothers? "Whosoever shall do the will of My Father which is in Heaven, the same is My brother, and sister, and mother." Matt. 12:50.
10. What commandment does God give regarding our parents? "Honor thy father and thy mother that thy days may be long in the land the Lord thy God giveth thee." Ex. 20:12.

THE BIBLE

To be Used in Connection With Song 44

1. What names has God's word? The Bible, Scriptures.
2. How many books in the Bible? Sixty-six.
3. How many books in the Old Testament? Thirty-nine.
4. How many books in the New Testament? Twenty-seven.
5. In what language was the Old Testament first written? Hebrew.
6. In what language was the New Testament first written? Greek.
7. How many people wrote the Bible? Thirty-six.

8. Who told them what to write? God's Holy Spirit.
9. Repeat the books of the Old Testament.
10. Repeat the books of the New Testament.
11. Are we commanded to study the Bible? "Search the Scriptures, for these are they which testify of me."
12. How are we commanded to follow its teachings? "Be ye doers of the word and not hearers only."

THE PROMISES

1. What promise have we that Christ will receive us?
"Him that cometh unto Me I will in no wise cast out." John 6: 37.
2. What promise have we of God's care?
"If God so clothe the grass of the field which today is and tomorrow is cast into the oven, shall He not much more clothe you, O ye of little faith?" Matt. 6: 30.
3. What promise have we of guidance?
"I will instruct thee and teach thee in the way thou shouldst go. I will guide thee with mine eye." Ps. 32: 8.
4. How has God promised to provide for our needs?
"The Lord is my Shepherd, I shall not want." Ps. 23: 1.
5. What promise have we of forgiveness for sin?
"Though your sins be as scarlet, they shall be as white as snow." Isa. 1: 18.
6. What promise have we of Jesus' presence with us?
"Lo, I am with you alway, even unto the end of the world." Matt 28: 20.
7. What promise have we of strength?
"As thy days thy strength shall be."
8. What promise have we of peace?
"Peace I leave with you, my peace I give unto you." John 14: 27.
9. What promise have we of rest?
"Come unto me all ye that labor and are heavy laden, and I will give you rest." Matt. 11: 28.
10. What promise have we of a home in Heaven.

"In my Father's house are many mansions. If it were not so, I would have told you." John 14: 2.

THE APOSTLES

1. How many apostles were there? Twelve.
2. What are their names? Peter, Andrew, James, the son of Zebedee, John, Philip, Bartholomew, Thomas, Matthew, James, the son of Alpheus, Thaddeus, Simon, Judas.
3. Who were the three who were nearest to Jesus? Peter, James and John.
4. Who was a tax-gatherer? Matthew.
5. Who were fisherman? Peter, Andrew, James and John.
6. Who denied Christ? Peter.
7. Who betrayed Him. Judas.
8. Who was the doubting disciple? Thomas.
9. To whom did Jesus say, "Have I been so long time with you and yet hast thou not known me?" Philip.
10. What is Christ's rule for discipleship? "If any man will come after me, let him deny himself and take up his cross and follow me." (Matt. 16: 24.)

THE MESSENGERS

Easter exercise for Primary children, each of whom should carry the flower mentioned in the verse assigned. A pretty effect is obtained if hairbows and sashes wore correspond in color with the flowers. At the close of each recitation, the plant should be placed on a low stand or table so that when the exercise is complete, the flowers as arranged will form part of the platform decorations.

First child with daffodils:
These daffodils like yellow gold,
The story of the Easter told,
For in their colors gayly clad
They said, " 'Tis Eastertime, be glad!"

Second child with purple hyacinths:
These hyacinths of purple hue,

Have told the Easter story too,
The purple bells their fragrance fling,
To tell of Christ the conquering King.

Third child with pink blossoms:
These blossoms that the trees adorn,
Bring tidings of the Easter morn,
That dawn that glowed in Eastern sky,
To tell of joy and gladness nigh.

Fourth child with lily:
This lily pure and snowy white,
Tells tidings of that morn so bright,
For like an angel wond'rous fair,
It heralds Easter everywhere.

Fifth child with fern:
In this little fern so green
Easter's happy news is seen,
Slumbering through the winter night
Now it wakes to Easter light.

ALL
Easter messages so fair,
We are finding everywhere,
Telling us so clear and plain
Jesus Christ is risen again.

LITTLE LAD OF GALILEE

Dialogue for one child and class or for two children. It may be used in connection with a blackboard lesson by drawing pictures of loaves, fishes, and baskets.

Little lad of Galilee
To your home returning,
Have you been beside the sea
Of the Master learning?

BOY
Yes, I lingered on the shore,
With the throng who harkened,
Wond'ring even more and more,
Till the shadows darkened.

CLASS
Little lad, little lad,
Ever mindful be,
Of the loving Christ who taught
By the sunlit sea.

Class Repeat

Little lad of Galilee,
We have heard it spoken
That He came a King to be,
Wond'rous works His token.

BOY
Fish I had and loaves of bread,
And I let Him take them,
All that multitude were fed,
When He blessed and brake them.

Little lad of Galilee
Did your scant store feed them?
For you gave so willingly
When the Lord did need them.

BOY
Yes, my loaves and fishes small,
Gave I not complaining,
And they were enough for all,
Basketsful remaining.

A WELCOME, DEAR CRADLE ROLL BABY

(This may be recited when a cradle roll baby visits the class.)
A welcome, dear cradle roll baby,
We give a glad greeting to you.
The Lord Whom we love,
Once came from above,
A dear little Baby like you!

A welcome, dear cradle roll baby,
Our songs for a greeting shall be.
Our Saviour so dear,
Our praises will hear,
For the Friend of the children is He

A welcome, dear cradle roll baby,
To this our dear Sunday School home.
When older you grow,
You'll join us, we know,
We hope that each Sunday you'll come

LITTLE RAYS OF SUNLIGHT

Little rays of sunbeams bright,
Shining with a golden light,
Bringing gladness and delight,
You and I may be!

Little blossoms sweet and fair,
Bringing beauty everywhere,
Kept by God the Father's care,
You and I may be!

Little helpers day by day,
Doing good along the way,
Helping others as we may,
You and I may be!

O, there's much that we can do,
Work for me and work for you,
Loving helpers, loyal true,
You and I may be!

Jesus is Born.

G. W. PAYN.   ARTHUR WILTON.

1. This is the song the an-gels sang, "Je-sus is born! Je-sus is born!"
2. Who were the first to hear the cry, "Je-sus is born? Je-sus is born?"

O - ver the world the cho-rus rang, Je-sus is born to - day.
Shepherds who gaz'd in - to the sky Heard it on Christmas morn.

CHORUS.

Glad bells were ring - ing, Bright an - gels sing - ing,

Brought us the news on Christ-mas morn, "Je - sus is born!"

Recitation.

Follow the Right.

When you're in doubt which way to take,
  Follow the Right.
Make this resolve that none can shake,
  Follow the Right to-day.

Scatter kind thoughts and words and deeds,
  Follow the Right.

Safe is the path where Duty leads,
  Follow the Right to-day.

God is the guide upon this road,
  Follow the Right.
Ever His help has He bestowed,
  Follow the Right to-day.

—ALICE JEAN CLEATOR.

At Easter Time.

Emma van Cleve Skillman. J. Lincoln Hall.

1. Tho' Je-sus lov'd them more than life They nail'd Him to the tree,
2. But Je-sus was not bound by death, He rose on Eas-ter day;
3. Yes, Je-sus died up-on the tree, To save our souls from sin;

They pierc'd His side, His hands, His feet, His love they could not see.
Our Sav-iour reigns in heav'n a-bove, And guides us on our way.
We'll o-pen now to Him our hearts, And bid Him en-ter in.

CHORUS.

At Eas-ter-time, glad Eas-ter-time, We sing in His dear name;

He is our Christ in life, in death, His love is e'er the same.

The Lord's Prayer.

Matt. 6 : 9–13.   Gregorian.

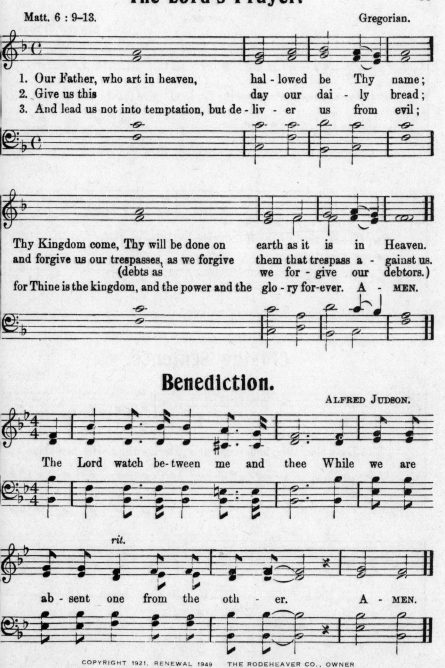

1. Our Father, who art in heaven,   hal - lowed be   Thy   name;
2. Give us this   day our dai - ly   bread;
3. And lead us not into temptation, but de - liv - er us   from evil;

Thy Kingdom come, Thy will be done on   earth as it is   in   Heaven.
and forgive us our trespasses, as we forgive   them that trespass a - gainst us.
        (debts as   we for - give our debtors.)
for Thine is the kingdom, and the power and the glo - ry for-ever. A - MEN.

Benediction.

ALFRED JUDSON.

The Lord watch be-tween me   and   thee While we   are

rit.

ab - sent one from the   oth - er.   A - MEN.

Praise.

(Sentence.)

ALFRED JUDSON.

Praise ye the Lord : Praise ye the Lord ; O give thanks un - to His name,

For He is good, for He is good ; Praise ye Him, praise ye Him.

Closing Sentence.

ALFRED JUDSON.

The Lord bless thee, and keep thee ; The Lord make His face shine up -

on thee, and give thee peace, and give thee peace. A-MEN, A-ME

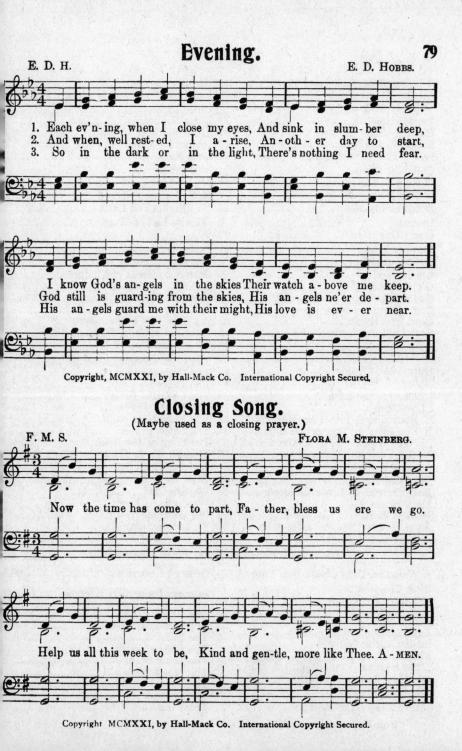

Evening.

E. D. H.   E. D. HOBBS.

1. Each ev'n-ing, when I close my eyes, And sink in slum-ber deep,
2. And when, well rest-ed, I a-rise, An-oth-er day to start,
3. So in the dark or in the light, There's nothing I need fear.

I know God's an-gels in the skies Their watch a-bove me keep.
God still is guard-ing from the skies, His an-gels ne'er de-part.
His an-gels guard me with their might, His love is ev-er near.

Closing Song.
(Maybe used as a closing prayer.)

F. M. S.   FLORA M. STEINBERG.

Now the time has come to part, Fa-ther, bless us ere we go.

Help us all this week to be, Kind and gen-tle, more like Thee. A-MEN.

INDEX.

Index of Recitations, Exercises, Etc.

(Songs for Little Singers, No. 3.)